Noah's Ark

Illustrated by Henry Ng
Colored by Benjamin Milam,
Julie Risko Neely, and Casey Sanborn
Written by Leslie Lindecker

*Read along to hear the story of Noah and his ark. You will know
it is time to turn the page when you hear this sound….
Now let us find out what happened a very long time ago.*

1

Noah was a good man who had loved God all his life. God blessed Noah with a wonderful wife, and together they had three sons. The sons grew up and married women who were like daughters to Noah. Noah thanked God every day for his good long life.

One day Noah told his wife, "God spoke to me in a dream last night. He told me he has a special plan for us."

Noah's wife loved her husband, and she believed God had spoken to him. "Come, listen to your father!" she called to their sons who were working outside.

Noah's sons and their wives gathered around
Noah to listen to him. Noah told them about his dream.

"God is sad. He sees that the people of the earth
have become very wicked. He plans to wash the
earth clean and make it good again."

"But Father!" said Shem, Noah's oldest son.
"What about us?"

Noah smiled. "God wants us to build a big boat called an ark. It must be big enough for us all, and two of every animal on the earth."

"A boat? But Father, we do not live near any water!" Shem said.

Noah and his sons left the house. They began to gather wood.

"We must build this ark a special size," Noah told his sons. "It must be 300 cubits long, 50 cubits wide, and 30 cubits high. It will have a small window at the top and a large door in the side. The ark must have three decks to hold our family and all the animals."

"We are farmers, Father," said Ham, Noah's middle son. "We do not know how to build an ark."

"In my dream, God showed me how to build it," Noah said. "And I will show you."

Noah and his sons began to build the ark. They worked from dawn until dusk. Noah's wife and his sons' wives gathered food for the animals and for themselves.

Noah's neighbors were curious about what Noah was doing. Noah warned them about God's plan.

"Noah, you are crazy!" they laughed. "You are building a boat because of a dream? And you don't even live near the sea."

Noah shook his head and continued to work on his ark.

When the ark was finished, Noah and his family loaded the food onto the ark. Then they waited.

Suddenly they heard a rustling. They heard flapping. They heard slithering, tromping, nickering, whinnying, cawing, barking, and chirping. Noah and his family looked around.

From all directions animals came. They came in pairs, two of every animal. From big elephants and tall giraffes to tiny mice and dainty ladybugs, and all the birds and animals in between.

Noah and his family guided the animals onto the ark.

12

The ark became very full of animals. Birds perched in the rafters. Mice ran underfoot. Frogs hopped among the larger animals.

Noah told his family, "Close the big door and seal it tightly. Be sure all the animals are settled."

"What will happen now?" asked Japheth, the youngest son.

"God is going to wash the earth clean of wickedness," Noah said. "It is going to rain. The seas will rise. The rivers will overflow. All the earth will be covered with water. We will be floating on the water as God has planned."

14

It began to rain—a few drops at first, and then a shower. Sometimes it was a thunderstorm with lightning and loud crashes of thunder. Other times it was a steady pounding.

The seas began to swell over the beaches. The rivers rose over their banks and flooded the lands. Soon Noah heard the water lapping against the sides of the ark. Everyone felt the waters lift the ark off the land.

Inside the ark, the people and the animals were snug and safe.

Noah's wife joined Noah at the window.

"How long is it going to rain?" she asked.

"God said it is going to rain for forty days and forty nights," Noah said. "God will take care of us. Do not worry.

"I am too busy to be worried," his wife said with a smile. "With this many animals to take care of, I do not have time to worry!" Noah laughed with his wife and closed the window on the rain.

Noah and his family were very busy during their time on the ark. They fed the animals and kept them clean, which was hard work. The animals were used to running free, but there was not a lot of room to run on the ark.

"The monkeys are teasing the lions," Shem told Noah.

"The dogs are chasing the cats," Ham told Noah.

"The turtles are racing the porcupines," Japheth told Noah.

Noah laughed and shook his head. "God is good to us," he said, and went back to practicing the bird calls the songbirds taught him.

After forty days and nights, the rain stopped. Noah and his wife peeked out of the upper window. Water was all they could see.

"We will check again soon," Noah said. A month passed. Another month passed. The sun came out. Noah opened the window again. He held a dove gently in his hands.

"Fly out, little dove," Noah said. "Find land and come back to me."

The dove flew away. She could not find land. She flew back to the ark, and Noah took her in.

A week later, Noah sent the dove out again.

"Fly out, little dove," Noah said. "Find land and come back to me."

This time the dove came back with an olive branch in her beak. Noah laughed. His wife clapped. His sons cheered. The little dove had found dry land!

Soon, the mountaintops peeked up out of the water. Noah and his family were happy. They looked forward to their life in a blessed new world.

With a sudden thump, the ark came to a stop on top of a mountain.

Noah and his sons opened the big door on the side of the ark. All the animals, birds, and bugs ran, walked, hopped, and flew out of the ark. Noah and his family came out laughing and singing praises to God.